Only twice before since the coming of the white man has a mountain peak in the Pacific Northwest's Cascade Range erupted, but in prehistoric times thick blankets of lava and pumice covered the surface of Oregon and Washington.

The first modern-day eruption of this serene setting was a century and a quarter ago when a few pioneers and adventurers saw steam, ash and fiery lava spew from Mount St. Helens in Southwest Washington, a peak the Indians called Lawelatla, the smoking mountain. Those eruptions continued for a decade before the snowcapped peak fell into long sleep.

The second occurred at Mount Lassen, the southernmost peak of the Cascade Range, in Northern California, in 1914 and continued until 1921.

The third eruption of this era began March 27 of this year on the summit of Mount St. Helens just 45 miles north of Portland. Towering clouds of steam, gas and ash have intrigued Northwesterners and, indeed, the entire world ever since.

This album is the story in pictures and prose of this reawakened volcano of the picturesque Cascades.

J. Richard Nokes, Editor of The Oregonian, Portland, Oregon

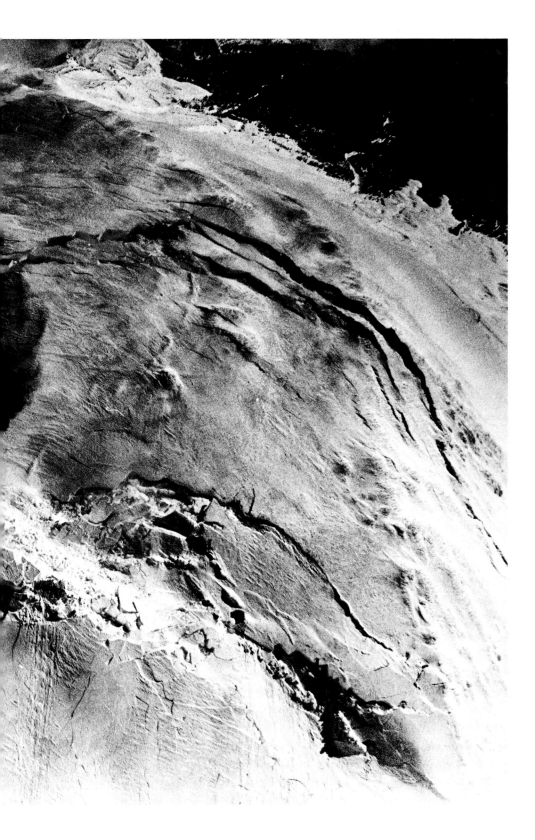

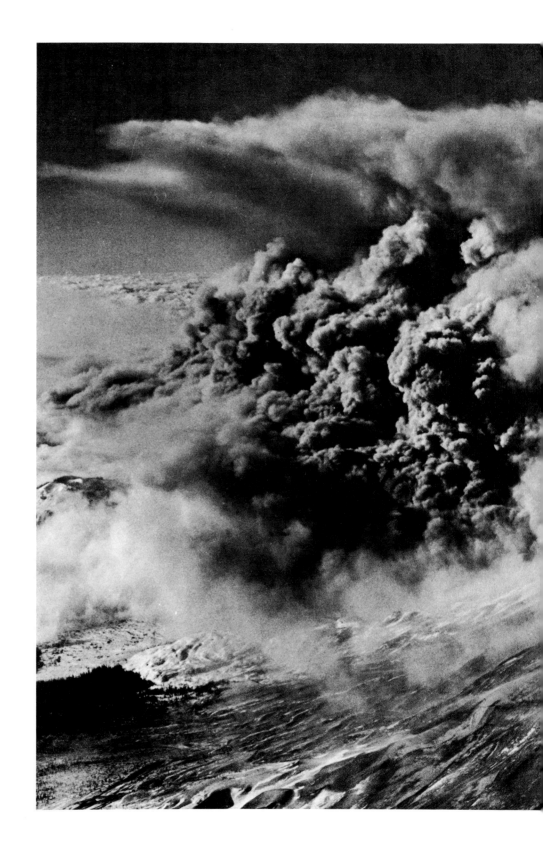

11

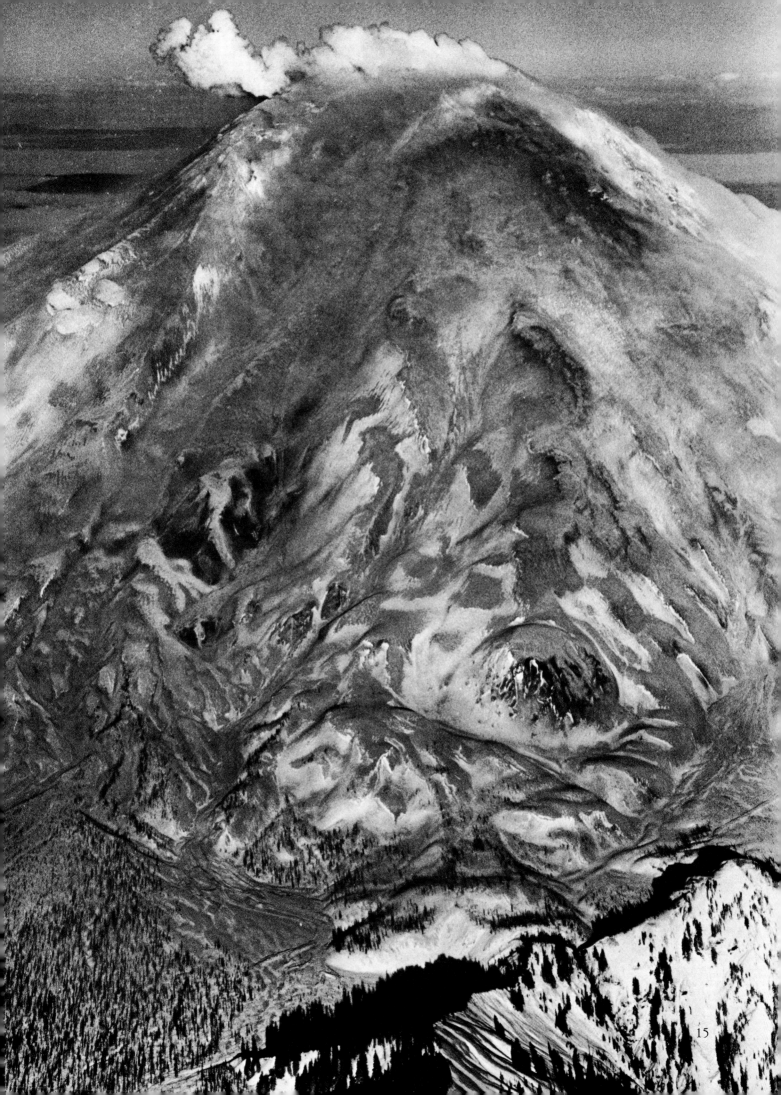

15

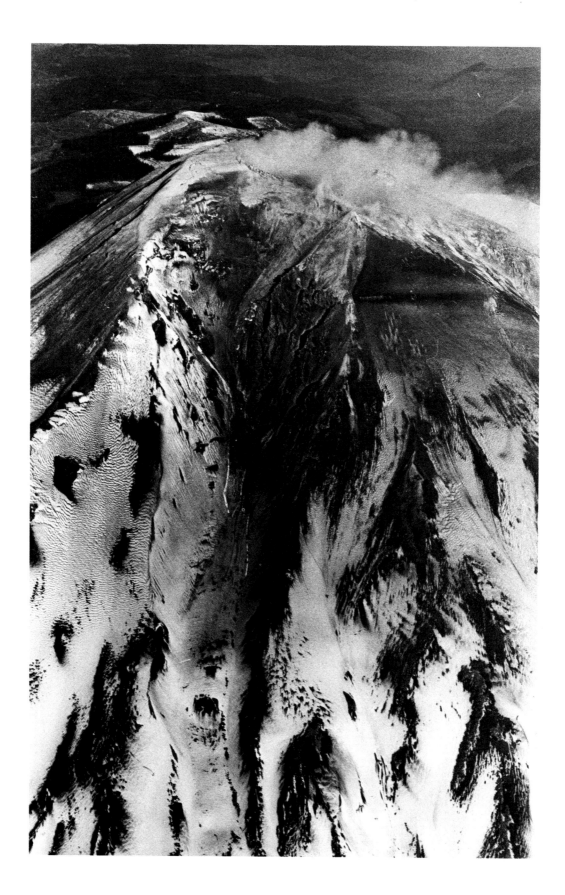

19

24

31

A LONG SLEEP COMES TO AN END

"Eruption is likely within the next 100 years, possibly before the end of this century . . ."

T hat was the prediction published by Dwight R. (Rocky) Crandell and Donal R. Mullineaux, U.S. Geological Survey volcanic hazards specialists, in a report released in March, 1975 after years of study of 9,677-foot Mount St. Helens, youngest and shyest of the queens of the Cascades in Southwestern Washington.

But neither prophet believed his ears when Charles Tonn, U.S. Forest Service ranger at Spirit Lake called them Thursday, March 20, 1980 at their Boulder, Colo., laboratory to tell them that the sleeping beauty was actually showing signs of awakening from her long sleep. Tonn said quakes had been felt at the north foot of the mountain. But the geologists passed off the tremor as just another "tectonic event"—normal shifting of the earth's crust.

Then Monday morning Mullineaux got an urgent call from Steven Malone, University of Washington seismologist, who had just returned from the mountain after planting portable seismographs on the spot. Malone reported the mountain was beginning to shake like a bowlful of jelly, punctuated by stronger jolts that "darned near shook the socks" off crusty old Harry Truman, "The Old Man of the Mountain," who had operated a resort on Spirit Lake, five airline miles from the peak, for 54 years and wasn't about to leave.

By Monday, March 24, swarms of quakes, up to 40 an hour, were being recorded at the U.S. Geophysical Laboratory at Newport, Wash., near the Idaho border, five of them greater than 4 on the Richter scale. But nothing seemed to be happening on the mountain and the scientists were wary about forecasting any eruption within the next week, month or year.

Tuesday, March 25, aerial observers spotted numerous avalanches of snow which had carved long trails for two or three miles down the east and northeast slopes of the mountain onto the Plains of Abraham. But no one got excited. Malone said "increased quake activity is no guarantee of an immediate eruption." The mountain had been dormant for 123 years—since April, 1857. Not even an active fumarole warned of its fiery past. The Forest Service had no plans to evacuate the 100 or so loggers and resort owners who lived within 15 miles of the peak.

Thursday, March 27 dawned dark with clouds. But about noon Mike Beard, reporter for Portland radio station KGW, spotted the top of the peak through a break in the clouds just in time to see history in the making. A plume of steam shot up through the ash and ice that had accumulated in the crater in the past 123 years. The Forest Service decided to close the mountain above the timberline to climbers and skiers because of the danger of avalanches.

During the night the clouds cleared away and "Little Fujiyama," remarkable for its resemblance to its bigger sister in Japan, posed like a queen in her robes of ermine in the bright moonlight. Then suddenly, about 2 a.m., Friday, March 28, the stately queen blew her top with a bang that was heard 'round the world. Observers on 3,926-foot Mitchell Peak, 15 miles away, heard a boom, followed by whistling sounds as white vapor rose lazily into the still air for nearly 20 minutes drifting slowly eastward. Booms were heard as far away as 20 miles to the south and west during the next day and night.

Sunday, March 30 dawned bright and clear and that was the setting the "Fire Mountain," as the Indians called it, chose to stage the most violent and spectacular eruption of its months-long temper tantrum. For nearly 20 minutes black ash boiled out of the crater in a dense black cloud, which drifted more than 100 miles to the southeast.

Some 38 Forest Service personnel in the ranger district headquarters 12 miles southeast of the peak were ordered to get out, "fast." Later the station was moved to Chelatchie Prairie Work Center about 20 miles south of the summit. About 300 Weyerhaeuser Company loggers were evacuated from the woods northwest of the mountain. Road blocks were set up about 35 miles from the mountain in all directions. Later loggers and cabin owners with legitimate business were permitted to pass the road blocks but advised not to remain in the danger area overnight.

The danger was not from possible lava flows, which would travel at a slow walk and not beyond the slopes of the mountain itself, but from fiery avalanches which could blast down the slopes at 100 miles an hour, the geologists warned. Mud slides, triggered by hot debris from the crater, mixed with melting snow, could also sweep down the southeast slopes, pouring into Swift Creek and Yale Reservoirs on the Lewis River, pushing water over the dams and causing floods. Mud slides hundreds of years ago had also cut off the Toutle River and valley that leads to Spirit Lake on the north side of the mountain.

While residents fled, geologists and the press and television crews from all over the world converged on the mountain, the first volcano in continental United States to blow its top since 10,457-foot Mount Lassen in northern California last spit steam and ash on Feb. 7, 1921. More than 20 U.S. Geological Service geologists were joined by another score of geologists from all over the world, including Haroun Tazieff, from Belgium, dean of world volcanologists.

The rejuvenated volcano continued to erupt with increasing violence, hidden most of the time by clouds. Quakes up to 4.9 on the Richter scale, enough to shake Harry Truman out of his favorite chair, shook the summit, leaving great crevasses in the thick ice that covered the summit. Blocks of ice 13 feet in all four dimensions, were hurled as high as 300 feet above the rim of the crater, leaving white tracks in the ash-covered snow as they rolled down the steep slopes.

It was not until clear weather permitted stereoscopic aerial pictures to be taken April 7 and 12 and studied in the U.S. Geological Survey photogrammetric laboratory that scientists realized the tremendous forces that had been at work. The pinnacle on the north side of the crater rim had been pushed up 250 feet. The glacier-covered rock of the mountain just above Forsythe Glacier on the north side of the peak had been pushed up and out 300 feet or more and was still in motion.

For three weeks the mountain lay napping, emitting only a little steam from fumaroles in its enlarged crater. But it continued to swell at the seams, to the accompaniment of continuous jolting quakes. By May 7, 1980, when the volcano resumed mild eruptions of steam and ash, the north face had swelled up and out more than 400 feet and was still moving.

But the first 53 days of earth-shaking activity proved to be "only a minor event in the life of a mountain like this."

Then, at 8:31 a.m. Sunday, May 18, 1980, it happened. The mountain finally blew its top—quite literally. With a bang that was heard as far north as Vancouver, B.C., the whole north face of the mountain a half mile wide and about a mile from top to bottom, shot out with the force of a half dozen atomic bombs.

The fiery avalanche—a river of incadescent lava and gas—shot down the mountain at speeds of 80 miles an hour or more, wiping out everything in its path. Fine volcanic ash, huge chunks of pumice and rock roared into Spirit Lake, five miles north and east of the crater, almost cutting the lake in two. The pyroclastic flow "nue ardente" or fiery avalanche created its own shock wave, which stripped trees of their foliage and laid them flat as far as 15 miles north of the peak. The hot gases melted snow and ice, triggering mud slides, which poured into the North and South Forks of the Toutle River, wiping out an estimated 50 miles of road and a half dozen bridges.

A cloud of ash shot up to 63,000 feet and drifted to the east coast, turning day to night as far east as Yakima, Wash., 90 miles to the east and closing airports as far east as Missoula, Mont., nearly 500 miles downwind. The top 1,277 feet of the peak was blown away, leaving the 9,677-foot peak only 8,400 feet above sea level by preliminary measurements.

The eruption continued with unabated fury for 24 hours, then tapered off. Scientists call it one of the most violent volcanic explosions in the continental United States since history began, comparable to a similar explosion of Mt. Lassen in northern California May 22, 1915.

What next? Volcanologists of the U.S. Geological Survey say "this is as violent as any eruption of St. Helens in the past 37,000 years. But the mountain may not be ready to go back to sleep yet."

—*Leverett Richards, of The Oregonian Staff*

WHY A VOLCANO?

The tremendous forces that cause volcanoes like Mount St. Helens to erupt are not fully understood. But scientists agree that the source of the volcano's energy lies 50 to 100 miles deep in the earth's mantle where temperatures of up to 2400 degrees, partly caused by radioactivity, melt the rock. The tremendous pressure forces the molten rock or magma up through cracks in the earth's crust.

As the magma or lava rises it melts the rock around it, forming magma chambers or reservoirs as close as two miles below the earth's surface. The heat that melts the rock releases gases, which add to the pressure that finally shoots the lava out of the volcano like shot from a cannon in the form of rocks, fine ash, coarser pumice or molten lava.

The Romans called them volcanoes after Vulcan, their god of fire. But there is no real fire in any volcanic eruption. Electric discharges or the incandescent glow of the molten rock reflected from the clouds of gas or steam give the appearance of fire. The "smoke" is really ash, carried aloft on the wings of the steam or hot gases.

RING OF FIRE

Mount St. Helens and the rest of the Cascade Range are part of the "Ring of Fire"—chain of volcanic mountains that ring the Pacific Ocean from South America through Canada and Alaska to Japan and beyond. Most are inactive, but eruptions occur every few years somewhere around this rim of the Pacific. Japan's Mount Fujiyama, St. Helens' sister peak, is part of this Ring of Fire.

Scientists believe volcanic action is concentrated around the shores of the Pacific because the crust of the earth is expanding and thrusting the floor of the ocean under the continents. The tremendous pressure tends to force magma or molten rock up through cracks in the earth's crust, forming volcanoes.

—*Leverett Richards, of The Oregonian Staff*

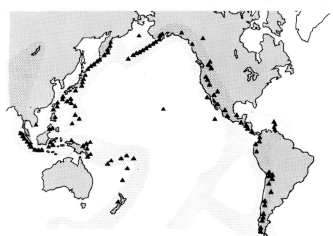

SHE WAS A VOLCANO
TO THE PIONEERS

Northwest pioneers in the 19th century were the first to write of eruptions of the volcanic Mount St. Helens, but there is no record of any harm to any of them.

The first recorded ascent of the beautiful peak, and mountaineers credit him, was made by the first editor of *The Oregonian*, Thomas J. Dryer, on Aug. 26, 1853 during the period of intermittent eruptions dating from 1842 to 1857.

Records of the Oregon Historical Society and *The Oregonian* of 1853 do not make clear just how many persons accompanied him, but there were several, and several horses. The trip took nearly two weeks in all, in and out, with the horses left behind at the base when the men made assault on the peak which took two days.

The great pioneer migration of 1843 brought Overton Johnson and William H. Winter to the Willamette valley. They wrote:

"Mount St. Helens, a lofty snow-capped volcano, rises from the plain, and is now burning. Frequently, the huge columns of black smoke may be seen, suddenly bursting from its crater, at the distance of thirty or forty miles."

The diary of Rev. George Cary of May 30, 1844, as he came up the Columbia River by small sailing ship, reported:

"We have a very distant view of a volcano in action, throwing up clouds of smoke. On further inquiry I have learned that this volcano is in Mount Helen (sic) itself, and that either the snow is diminishing or the soot settling upon the white covering of the mountain presents the appearance of wasting snow.

"The falling ashes or soot have been seen and gathered from boards or anything of a smooth surface, say 50 miles from the crater.

"We will all gaze for a while."

Peter H. Burnett in 1844 wrote at the mouth of the Wallamette (sic) "as you enter the Columbia. From Linnton you have a very fair and full view of St. Helen about 50 miles distant. But it looks as if it was within reach.

"The peak is very smooth, and in the form of a regular cone, and nearly, if not quite, as tall as Mount Hood and also covered with perpetual snow. This mountain is now a burning volcano. It commenced about a year since.

"The crater is on the side of the mountain, about two thirds of the distance from its base. On the 16th day of February, 1844, being a beautiful and clear day, the mountain burned most magnificently. The dense masses of smoke rose up in one immense column, covering the whole crest of the mountain in clouds. Like other volcanoes, it burns at intervals.

"On one side of the mountain, near its top, is a large black object admidst the pure white snow around it. This is supposed to be the mouth of a large cavern." (This was probably the crater of the eruptions.)

Robert Caufield of Oregon City wrote to a brother in Ireland April 1, 1848: "There have been two emptyings of this mountain since we came here. The report we could hear distinctly and the reflections seen in the sky at night."

None of the old descriptions from records of the Oregon Historical Society say anything about an earthquake. But all of these observations were from some miles away. In the new 1980 eruptions, the earthquakes were localized around the mountain itself, but sophisticated sensory gear has been monitoring them both close at hand and many miles away.

A Canadian artist, Paul Kane, visited the Northwest in March of 1847, and on March 26 sketched Mount St. Helens from the mouth of the Lewis River, about 35 miles from the peak.

"There was not a cloud visible in the sky at the time I commenced my sketch," he wrote, "and not a breath of air was perceptible; suddenly a stream of white smoke shot up from the crater of the mountain and hovered a short time over its summit; it then settled down like a cap."

He later made a painting from his sketch, a nighttime scene, which included a canoe of naked Indians. The painting now hangs in the Royal Ontario Museum of Archeology in Toronto.

Editor Dryer's own diarylike account of what mountaineers now credit as the first ascent of the peak was printed in *The Oregonian* of Sept. 3, 1853. It recounts the trip by horseback from Vancouver, the many game, including grouse, elk, deer and panthers. As they approached the snowy slopes finally after several days of journey, he wrote with feeling:

"The appearance upon a near approach is sublimely grand and impossible to describe. The blackened piles of lava which were thrown into ridges hundreds of feet high in every imaginable shape of primitive formation. The mountain is seeming to lift its head above and struggling to be released from its compressed position impressed the mind of the beholder with the power of omnipotence and the insignificance of human power when compared with that of Nature's God.

"Above all stands a tower of eternal rock and snow apparent stretching its head high above the clouds and looking down with disdain upon all beneath. The glaring sunbeams upon the snow of a thousand winters served by contrast to make the immense piles of lava blacker than they otherwise would.

"We commenced the ascent at once on the south side by climbing up the cliffs of lava toward a small cluster of spruce trees which stand a short distance from the line of perpetual snow.

"After several hours of hard toil we reached this point and finding a few sticks of dry wood tended a fire and made our camp for the night. We here supplied ourselves with water by melting snow.

"We found the night cold and extremely uncomfortable. Our party did not find much repose. And as the eastern sky commenced to show the approach of day we left the camp and pursued our way upward.

"The higher we ascended the more difficult our progress. Suffice it to say that by constant and persevering effort, we were enabled to reach the highest pinnacle of the mountain soon after meridian.

"The atmosphere produced a singular affect (sic) upon all the parties. Each face looked pale and sallow. And all complained of a strange ringing in the ears. It appeared as if there were hundreds of fine-toned bells ringing in our ears. Blood started from our noses and all of us found respiration difficult.

"With this exception we all felt well. It would be futile to attempt to give our readers a correct idea of the appearance of the vast extent of country visible from the top of the mountain.

"The crater has been represented to be on the southwest side of the mountain, which is not the case. We took the bearing from the top with a compass and found it to be on the northwest side.

"The smoke was continually issuing from its mouth, giving unmistakable evidence that the fire was not extinguished. There is much more snow on the north side than on the south side. On the latter it is bare in spots, while on the former it is hundreds of feet deep.

"We examined fissures on the snow several rods across which extended a great length along the side of the mountain and on throwing a stone down, hear it strike a long distance from us.

"After spending sufficient time to see what was to be seen and building a pyramid of loose stones on that highest spot of level earth and ashes, we commenced our descent and reached our camp at four in the afternoon, tired and worn out in body and boots.

"At dark we reached the timber and camped for the night. The next morning we left our camp for our home which we reached in four days . . . .

"We are fully satisfied with our trip and are willing hereafter to devote our time to matters requiring less labor and fraught with more of the comforts of life than we have experienced on this trip to the top of Mount Saint Helens."

—Ann Sullivan, of The Oregonian Staff

RICHTER SCALE

The Richter scale is a measure of the amount of energy involved in an earthquake, as measured by calibrated seismographs.

It is a logarithmic scale, in which each higher number on the scale represents approximately 31 times the energy of the preceding number. A 4 on the Richter scale is 31 times as violent as 3. A magnitude of 2 is about the lowest that is ordinarily reported felt by humans.

The 1906 earthquake which destroyed San Francisco in 1906, measured 8.3 on the Richter scale. The Good Friday Quake which killed more than 100 and changed the face of a wide area of Alaska in March, 1964, measured 8.5 on the Richter scale.

The worst ever recorded in the world measured 8.9 on the Richter scale—off the coast of Colombia and Ecuador Jan. 31, 1906 and off the east coast of Honshu, Japan March 2, 1933.

—Leverett Richards, of The Oregonian Staff

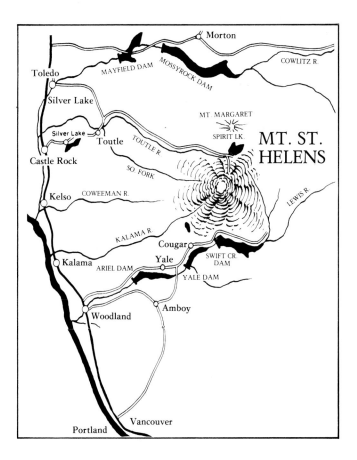

OUR MOUNTAIN, "LAWELATLA"

I sit here this morning, looking towards our mountain, Lawelatla, my thoughts turn back in time to the stories that have been handed down to us over the years by our ancestors.

My people, the Cowlitz Indians, were very close to our mountain, both physically and spiritually. The Cowlitz hunted, fished and lived at the base of the mountain, and it was known to be "their mountain."

Mountains are great persons to our Indian people. Mount St. Helens has always been know to the Cowlitz Indians as Lawelatla ("Person from Whom Smoke Comes"). Each time the mountain rumbled and belched smoke it was speaking to our people. Indians have great respect for Mother Earth and every living thing. Each rock, tree, stream, bird, fish and animal has its own spirit which speaks to them and tells of the things that are happening all around them. The mountains have the greatest, most powerful spirits of all.

The word "Cowlitz" means "Capturing the Medicine Spirit." It was a part of our culture for every young man to go out into the woods and seek his own tamanawash (his guiding spirit to guide him throughout his life). Some would receive a raven spirit, the wisest of all the birds and the first to know all about the land. Others would receive a bear spirit, representing physical strength. They might receive the spirit of the beaver, eagle, frog or some other animal or bird. When a young man wanted a powerful spirit, he would go to Lawelatla, fasting and praying while waiting for his tamanawash. Sometimes this might take many days.

The mountain was used in many ways: for food gathering, hunting, fishing and spirit quests. The most important use was for the spirit quest.

What do our people feel today as they once again hear their mountain speaking? Many of them believe that the present eruptions are an expression of spiritual powers contained in the mountain. A large number of our dead ancestors have been buried there, and white men, people of no morals or conscience, have desecrated their graves by digging them up for the artifacts they might find therein. I sometimes wonder how they would react if we should dig up their grandmothers' graves. Some of our people believe the present eruptions are the spirits of our departed ancestors, rising up in divine retribution against these menacing white invaders.

—Roy Wilson, Chairman of the Cowlitz Tribe

ACKNOWLEDGEMENTS:

"Mount St. Helens, The Volcano", copyright 1980 by The Oregonian Publishing Company, Portland, Oregon. Prepared and designed for *The Oregonian* by Charles S. Politz, Design Council, Inc.

We want to thank Jim Vincent, Photo Editor of *The Oregonian* and photographers Randy Wood, Tim Jewett, Bob Ellis, Brent Wojahn, Dale Swanson, Michael Lloyd, Wes Guderian, Don Wilson and Kraig Scattarella of *The Oregonian* and Jack Smith of the *Associated Press,* Ray Atkeson and writers Leverett G. Richards and Ann Sullivan and others on the news staff of *The Oregonian* who gave their support and cooperation. We also thank Roy Wilson, chairman of the Cowlitz Indian Tribe. Also a special thanks to Denise Meyer of *The Oregonian,* for her help.

Al McCready
Managing Editor, The Oregonian

Joseph R. Bianco
Sunday Editor, The Oregonian
Editor of "Mount St. Helens, The Volcano."

LEGEND

Cover: The first big eruption, March 30, 1980.
Photo by Randy Wood, The Oregonian

Inside
front cover: During the eruption, March 30, 1980.
Photo by Randy Wood, The Oregonian

Page 2: The summit of Mount St. Helens taken in 1968.
Photo by Jim Vincent, The Oregonian

Page 3: Serene Mount St. Helens reflected in Spirit Lake before 1980 volcanic activity.
Photo by Ray Atkeson, famed Northwest photographer

Pages 4-5: Crater appears, March 27, 1980, after earlier small eruption.
Photo by Michael Lloyd, The Oregonian

Pages 6-7: Plume of smoke, steam and ash, seen by moonlight, 1:48 a.m., March 28, 1980.
Photo by Brent Wojahn, The Oregonian

Pages 8-9: End of first big eruption, Mount St. Helens, March 30, 1980.
Photo by Randy Wood, The Oregonian

Page 10: Mount St. Helens clouded by a veil of ashes, March 30, 1980
Photo by Jack Smith, Associated Press

Page 11: Black and white smoke zooms upwards from the volcano, March 30, 1980.
Photo by Randy Wood, The Oregonian

Pages 12-13: Mushroom-shaped cloud forms over Mount St. Helens. Mount Rainier in background, March 30, 1980.
Photo by Jack Smith, Associated Press

Page 14: Volcano turns silent, April 1, 1980. Mount Hood in background.
Photo by Jack Smith, Associated Press

Page 15: Beginning of the first big eruption, March 30, 1980.
Photo by Randy Wood, The Oregonian

Page 16: Mount St. Helens with ash blowing. Not an eruption.
Photo by Jim Vincent, The Oregonian

Page 17: During first big eruption, March 30, 1980.
Photo by Randy Wood, The Oregonian

Pages 18-19: An eruption of steam from the volcano has just ended, April 1, 1980.
Photo by Michael Lloyd, The Oregonian

Pages 20-21: What appears to be an eruption is a cloud of fine volcanic ash, April 2, 1980.
Photo by Jim Vincent, The Oregonian

Pages 22-23 White cloud displays gray color of the volcanic ash from May 18, 1980 eruption. Mud slides and heat from eruption have melted the mountain's snow cap.
Photo by Bob Ellis, The Oregonian

Page 24: Billowy cloud of smoke and ash from May 18, 1980 eruption, considered to be the most violent Mount St. Helens eruption in the last 30,000 years.
Photo by Bob Ellis, The Oregonian

Page 25: Mountain has face change. Two craters merge into one, April 2, 1980.
Photo by Jim Vincent, The Oregonian

Pages 26-27: Mount St. Helens seen from Portland's West Hills, April 4, 1980.
Photo by Tim Jewett, The Oregonian

Pages 28-29: Plane monitors eruptions on Mount St. Helens, April 4, 1980.
Photo by Dale Swanson, The Oregonian

Pages 30-31: Plane passes directly over 1,700 foot crater, April 10, 1980.
Photo by Jack Smith, Associated Press

Page 36: Oil painting of erupting Mount St. Helens in March, 1847 by Canadian artist, Paul Kane. Original in Royal Ontario Museum of Archaeology, Toronto, Canada.

Page 38: Stratus cloud intersects this view of erupting Mount St. Helens taken from the west side of mountain, May 18, 1980.
Photo by Don Wilson, The Oregonian

Page 39: Top of Mount St. Helens has been blown off with the force of the May 18, 1980 eruption.
Photo by Don Wilson, The Oregonian

Pages 40-41: View reveals decapitated Mount St. Helens, a once-forested hillside, and tons of ash in the river valley. Trickle at bottom of hill is all that remains of South Toutle River, May 19, 1980.
Photo by Kraig Scattarella, The Oregonian

Page 42: Forty feet of volcanic ash and mud from May 18, 1980 eruption cover valley of Toutle River's North Fork, about five miles from erupting Mount St. Helens.
Photo by Wes Guderian, The Oregonian

Page 43: Fiery avalanche of incandescent lava and gas flattened and stripped the timber of its foliage in May 18, 1980 explosion.
Photo by Wes Guderian, The Oregonian

Pages 44-45: Massive darkened crater is all that remains of what was once a beautiful snow-capped cone. Old landmarks can no longer be distinguished. This destruction was photographed May 20, 1980.
Photo by Wes Guderian, The Oregonian

Pages 46-47: Mountain vents steam through newly formed crater, May 19, 1980.
Photo by Wes Guderian, The Oregonian

Inside
back cover: Mount St. Helens is dwarfed by billows of ash and smoke sent nine miles into the air. The ash and smoke cloud blackened several states on its journey east of the volcano.
Photo by Don Wilson, The Oregonian

Back cover: Veil of ash covers snow, April 10, 1980.
Photo by Dale Swanson, The Oregonian

42

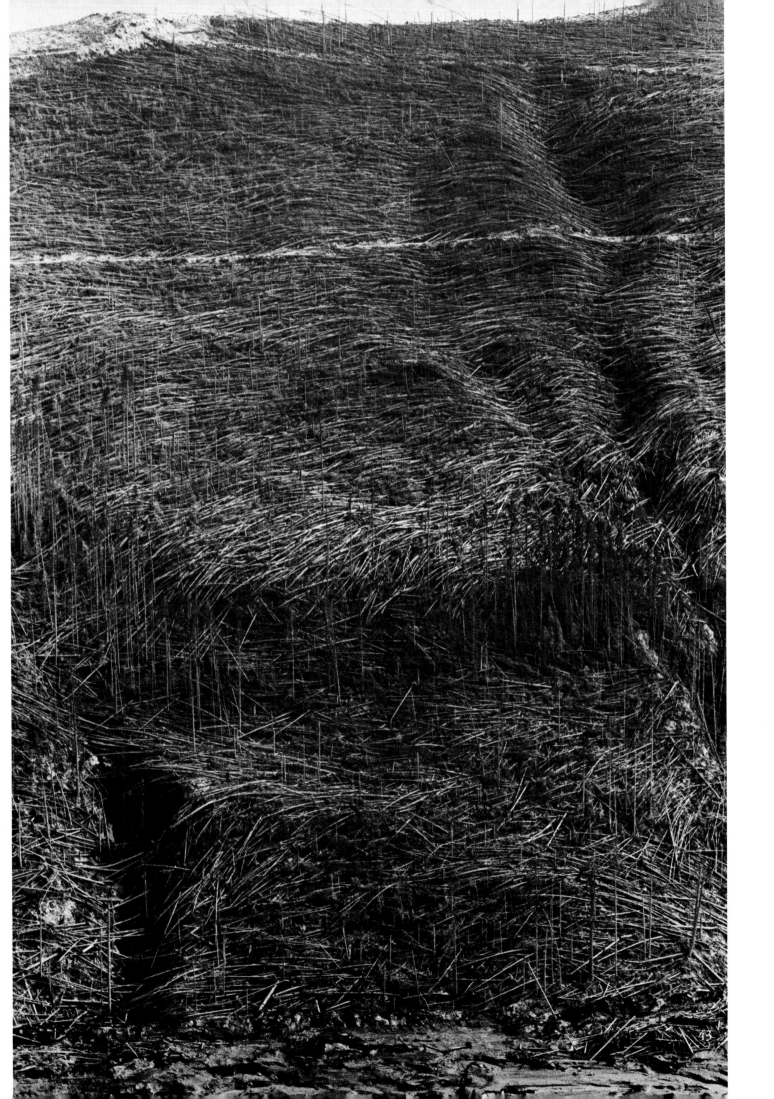